I ♥ RAINBOWS

Buster Books

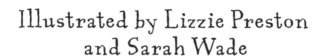

Illustrated by Lizzie Preston and Sarah Wade

Edited by Jonny Leighton
Cover Design by Derrian Bradder
Designed by Jade Moore

First published in Great Britain in 2021 by Buster Books, an imprint of
Michael O'Mara Books Limited, 9 Lion Yard, Tremadoc Road, London SW4 7NQ

 www.mombooks.com/buster   Buster Books   @BusterBooks   @Buster_Books

ISBN: 978-1-78055-775-5

2 4 6 8 10 9 7 5 3 1

This book was printed in April 2021 by
Bell & Bain Limited, 303 Burnfield Road, Thornliebank,
Glasgow, G46 7UQ, United Kingdom

MIX
Paper from
responsible sources
FSC® C007785

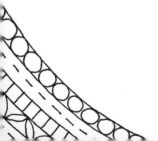
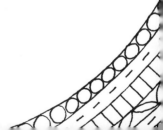

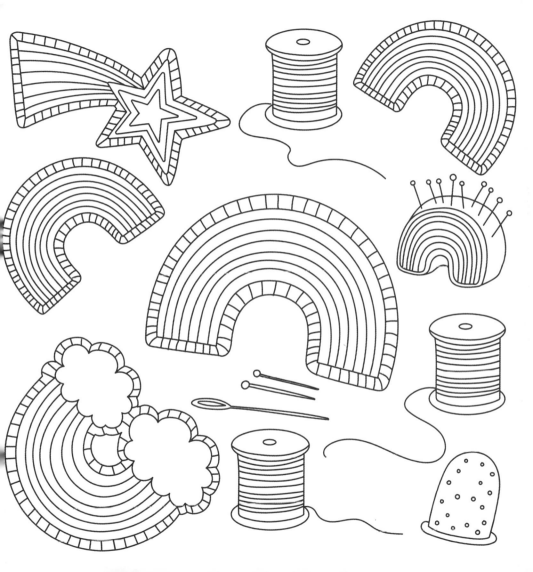

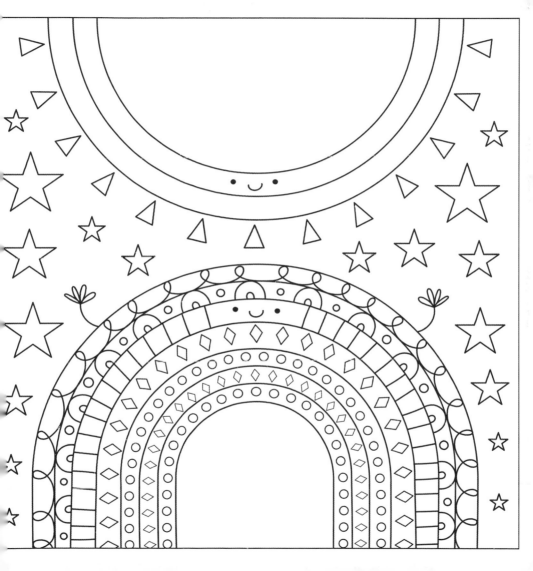

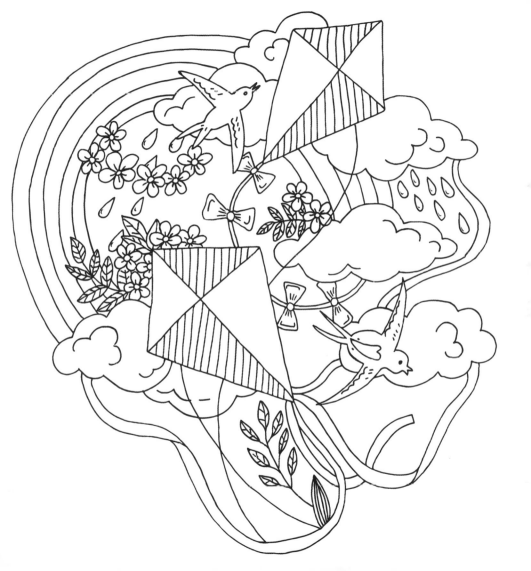